CONTENTS

War G~ ~~~
by Michael ~~~~~~

CW00853913

CREDITS

Published by Scholastic Ltd,
Villiers House,
Clarendon Avenue,
Leamington Spa,
Warwickshire CV32 5PR
Text © Alan Howe
© 1998 Scholastic Ltd
1 2 3 4 5 6 7 8 9   8 9 0 1 2 3 4 5 6 7

Author Alan Howe
Editor Clare Gallaher
Series designer Lynne Joesbury
Designer Glynis Edwards
Illustrations Michael Foreman
Cover illustration Michael Foreman
Designed using QuarkXpress

British Library Cataloguing-in-Publication Data
A catalogue record for this book is available
from the British Library.

ISBN 0-590-53838-1

ACKNOWLEDGEMENTS

Carcanet Press Ltd for the use of 'Winter Warfare'
by Edgell Rickword from *Behind the Eyes* ©
1976, Edgell Rickword (1976, Carcanet Press).
T & V Holt Associates for permission to reproduce
a postcard entitled 'Don't worry, I'll soon be
back' from the postcard collection of Tonie
and Valmai Holt: Picture Postcards 1869–1945.
Imperial War Museum for the use of the
photograph 'British troops go into action.
Western Front, Spring 1917' © Imperial War
Museum PC0032, neg. no. Q5100.
The Royal Welch Fusiliers for the use of an
extract from *The War the Infantry Knew
1914–1919* by Captain JC Dunn © 1987, The
Royal Welch Fusiliers (1987, Jane's Publishing
Co. Ltd; first published in 1938 by PS King Ltd in
a private edition).
Pavilion Books for the reproduction of the
covers from *War Game* by Michael Foreman
© 1989, 1993 Michael Foreman (1989, 1993,
Pavilion Books; 1995, Puffin Books) and the
supply of a black and white photograph of
Michael Foreman © Michael Dyer Associates Ltd.
Society of Authors as the Literary Representative
of the Estate of AE Housman for the use of a
verse from 'Here Dead Lie We' from *More Poems*
© 1936, The Society of Authors (published
posthumously).

Every effort has been made to trace copyright
holders and the publishers apologize for any
inadvertent omissions.

INTRODUCTION

War Game
by Michael Foreman

WHAT'S THE PLOT OF THE STORY?

In autumn 1914, war was declared on Germany. Recruiting posters were put up all over Britain, and young men were encouraged to join the army. Everyone thought that the war would be over by Christmas. *War Game* tells the story of a group of young men, all players in their village football team, who join up together, and set off for France and the 'great adventure' of the war. But when they get there, they find that the reality of fighting in the trenches is anything but a game...

WHAT'S SO GOOD ABOUT THIS BOOK?

War Game is a simple story about how a group of young, innocent farming lads are confronted with the horrific conditions and terrible brutality of the trenches in the First World War. But a central part of the story is also about how the spirit of Christmas overcomes hostilities, allowing an extraordinary event to happen. As well as a moving story, Michael Foreman's brilliant illustrations, and use of real posters and images from the time of the Great War, as it was called, help to bring the book to life.

ABOUT MICHAEL FOREMAN

You might know Michael Foreman as an illustrator of other writers' stories, but over the years he has written and illustrated a number of highly successful books of his own. Best known are perhaps *War Boy* and *After the War Was Over*, which tell the story of his early life growing up in Suffolk during the Second World War, as well as his anti-pollution book, *Dinosaurs and All That Rubbish*.

© Michael Dyer Associates

Everything he writes is always about something that matters to him, and many of his books are, in one way or another, against injustice and war, and celebrate the creativity and honesty of ordinary human beings.

Cover comparison

Cover A

Cover B

● Look at these two covers that have been designed for *War Game*. For each, look very closely and make a list of everything that you can see. Look very carefully at the hints that each cover gives the reader about the content of the book.

Cover A	Cover B

● Which cover do you prefer? Say why:

● Think about the title as well as the cover. What are your predictions about the book you are about to read?

What do you know about the First World War?

You might be surprised by how much information you already have in your head!

● Use the mind map to brainstorm everything you know about the world war that happened between 1914 and 1918. See if you can link information and ideas up by using the side branches. One has been done for you to give you the idea.

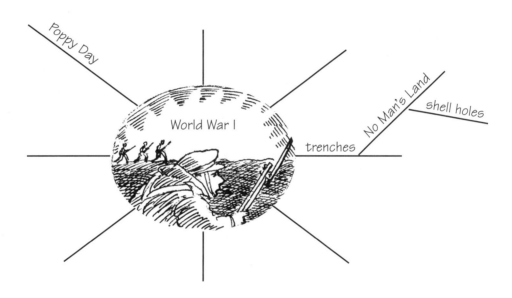

● Use your mind map to think up some questions you'd like to know the answers to about the First World War.

The greater game

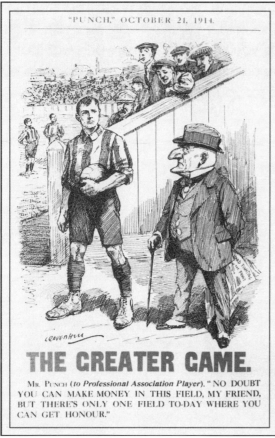

This poster, from a magazine called 'Punch', is printed on the page opposite the title page of the book. It was originally printed in 1914 at the start of the First World War. Look at it carefully.

● What is the point of the poster?

● What is the old man ('Mr Punch') really saying to the football player?

● What is 'the greater game'?

● Use a dictionary to look up these words:

	Dictionary definition
honour	
enlist	
patriotic	
recruit	

Getting a sense of the story

● These are the chapter headings in *War Game*. Read them carefully, then discuss with a partner what idea they give you about the story. Write your thoughts on a separate sheet of paper.

THE KICK-OFF   TO THE FRONT

THE ADVENTURE   NO MAN'S LAND

● Now read the first chapter up to '…as they wandered back along the dusty lane into the village'.

● Where is the opening to the story set? Find some of the words and phrases that tell you where the story begins and write them in the box.

● What do the young men think about the war that has just started? Read these pages again carefully, and then write their thoughts:

Freddie   Billy   Lacey   Will

Will's diary (1) The football game

● Read to the end of Chapter 1.

● Imagine that Will keeps a diary. In it, he records important events in his life, and describes his feelings and opinions.

As you read and think about *War Game*, you are going to write some pages of Will's diary. But first, you need to think about how diaries are written.

● Read these diary entries. See if you can work out some basic *rules* for diary writing.

Again the day was very hot. At 10.30, or soon after, we arrived at the village of Haussy. The whole Brigade halted and drew up in mass-formation on some grassland near the railway station. We remained there for a couple of hours at least. We

were in a hollow surrounded by low hills on the tops of which our cavalry patrols could be seen retiring, and being shelled while doing so... Nothing untoward happened, and about 1.30 we were off again.

Terrible bombing raids on Germany. Mr van Daan is grumpy. The reason: the cigarette shortage... Turkey's entered the war. Great excitement. Anxiously awaiting radio reports.

● Now add your rules to this list.

Rules for diary writing

1. Record your thoughts and feelings as well as events.
2. No need to write in complete sentences. For example, a diary entry might begin: 'Met my best friend, Luke today. Went into town.'

● You are ready to begin writing Will's diary (on your special diary sheet). Use your rules to write the page. Include important details from Chapter 1, such as:

• Will's thoughts about Saturday's football match
• What the lads talked about as they walked home
• Will's thoughts about the war starting; does he understand why it is being fought?
• Will's feelings about whether to join the army and go off to fight.

You could begin your page like this:

Sunday, 8th September 1914

Played our first game of football yesterday against Ambersham Utd. I scored the winner!

On the way back we...

Diary page

READ & RESPOND
9

A lot of explaining to do

● Read up to the words 'They had a lot of explaining to do when they got home that evening.'
Michael Foreman doesn't tell us what was actually said when the lads got home. He leaves it to our imagination. Your job is to write the 'missing' episode where Will arrives home and tells his family what he has done.

What does Will say? How do his parents (and grandparents or sisters perhaps?) reply? Are they pleased and proud of their son? Are they upset, worried, even angry? Or are there some mixed reactions?

● In a group of three or four, *improvise* the scene before you write it.
Then write the scene as a *script*, before presenting it to the rest of the class.
You could begin your scene like this:

WILL: I'm home, mother!
MOTHER: Where've you been till this hour of the evening?

Will's diary (2) To the Front

- Read up to '...and the long dry summer was over.'
- Write some more pages from Will's diary. They should cover:
- his time at the training camp
- the trip over the sea to France
- the journey through France to the Front.

Re-read these sections and look carefully at the pictures. Decide what details to include.

- To help you, make some *notes* first. Collect *factual* information and also make a note of Will's *thoughts* and *feelings*. Note down your findings on this chart.

	Facts	Will's thoughts and feelings
training camp		
sea crossing		
journey through France		

Remember your *rules* for diary writing. Write Will's diary for:

- **Wednesday, 13th October 1914 (You could begin:** I've had enough of this training camp. I thought...**)**
- **Monday, 3rd November 1914 (**Today we finally set off...**)**
- **Tuesday, 4th November 1914 (**When we arrived in France we were marched to a train. Then we set off through the countryside. It was...**)**

CHECK:

Have you included all the important details from this section of the book?
Have you included Will's feelings about the training camp, how he felt when he set off for France and the first day he travelled through the strange new country?

Then things began to change

● Read up to the words '…Just like fireworks.'

● The great adventure starts to become something different. Re-read the section below.

> Then things began to change. The roads became crowded with people moving back from the Front. The whole population seemed to be on the move. Families carried their children and pushed prams loaded with whatever they could salvage from their lives. No more cheering crowds. These people had seen war. Their homes had been blown to bits, their farms criss-crossed by armies, trenches, wire, and pock-marked by a million artillery shells. Will could hear the almost continuous sound of shellfire in the distance.
>
> They passed wagons full of wounded soldiers on their way back to England, and long lines of exhausted ragged troops sitting in the mud, rain and gathering darkness before being ordered back into the action.

● Use the passage to answer these questions.

Make a list of at least *three* things that have changed for Will, Freddie, Billy and Lacey:

Why are the roads full of people travelling?

What sorts of things do you imagine the people had in the prams?

The author uses some special words and phrases to show how war affects people's lives. These words and phrases have been circled in the passage. Explain in your own words what each of the words and phrases says about war to you.

salvage

criss-crossed by armies

pock-marked

continuous sound of shellfire

exhausted ragged troops

Can you find any more words or phrases in the passage that show that war is a disaster for ordinary people caught up in it? Write them here.

Will's Diary (3) The Front Line

● Read up to the words '...accompanied by cheers and boos.'

● Imagine that Will hasn't been able to find time to write in his diary for a few weeks. Now he sits down to record his impressions of life in the trenches.

Write a diary page that describes Will's shock at the reality of war. Does he still see it as a great adventure?
To help you to write the diary page, use these starting points for *drafting* your ideas on this sheet. Look back through the section you have read, and look carefully at the pictures.

© Imperial War Museum PC0032

10th December 1914

I have been in the trenches for several weeks now. Life here is

I was posted on sentry duty. Freddie and I had to

No Man's Land is

The enemy is only

Recently the weather has been getting worse. It has been raining. Because of this

I often think of home, and wish

● Now write your final version of Will's diary page, in your best handwriting. You could include some pencil sketches to help explain what his life is like at the Front.

CHECK:

Have you included Will's feelings about the war, and his longing to be safe at home?

Will's postcard – Christmas

● Read up to the words 'Good night, Fritz. We'll have another game.'

● Now read this letter from Lance Corporal Frank Callow to his parents.

Lance Corporal Frank Callow   *28/12/14*

My dear...

Thank you very much for the baccy and the plum pudding. All very fine and most welcome. I have just spent the most peculiar Christmas of my life - in the trenches! The weather and the past few weeks have been terrible, with heavy rain and wind, but we've all managed to keep our spirits up by thinking of home, and knowing that the war will soon be over. I'm lucky to be with such a very nice set of fellows. On Christmas Eve we had a sharp frost and everything froze over - it was quite beautiful, especially by moonlight. Please thank Nanny for the knitted socks - they came in most useful. All the guns stopped on Christmas Day - it was quiet and peaceful. We all received a present from the King and Queen of a lovely tobacco tin with the royal crest, and everyone had an extra allowance of rum. Strange to be celebrating Christmas, and then getting ready to fight each other the very next day.

Do give my best wishes to all in the village, and give an especial kiss to my dear sister Victoria.

I think of you often and long to be safe home soon.

Trust you are well,

Yours ever,

Frank

● Imagine Will writes a postcard home, describing how he spent Christmas Day 1914.
Write Will's postcard, using information from the book, but also try to copy the *style* of Lance Corporal Frank Callow's letter (the *way* it is written). You haven't much room on Will's postcard, so limit yourself to 50 words.

CARTE POSTALE

The ending

● Read to the end of the book.

● Can you find some examples where Michael Foreman compares the counter-attack to a game of football? Write the actual words here.

● Can you find some examples where you realize that this isn't a game any more? Write the actual words.

● 'Suddenly they all seemed to be tackled at once.' What do you think is happening here?

● Why do you think the writer describes the event in this way?

● At the end of the story, Will meets a wounded German soldier. Why do you think Foreman decides to include this? Try to think of at least *three* reasons why this is an effective way of ending the story.

● Look carefully at the illustrations on the last few pages. Explain how they add to the powerful feeling of the way the story ends. Write your thoughts on a separate sheet of paper.

No man's land

● Look back at the pictures of scenes in the trenches at the beginning of the final chapter.

Choose *one* of the pictures and look at it very carefully. You are going to work on a *word picture* – a short piece of descriptive writing, based on your chosen scene.

● First, make a list of words and phrases that describe the scene.

● Pick out a few things in the illustration and write comparisons for them. For example: 'a flare exploding in the night sky like a huge sun'.

● Now, using your notes and still looking closely at the picture, draft out your word picture of the scene. Make your writing as descriptive and vivid as you can, so that someone reading it would be able to imagine the scene clearly, and be able to identify your chosen illustration from the book.

Revise and change your draft paragraph as you wish, then write up your final version.

● Finally, with a partner or in a small group, take turns to read your word pictures. See if the others can identify the illustrations.

Those left behind

Back in England, Will's family waits anxiously for news.

● Imagine that you are Will. Draft a letter home, telling your family all your news since you arrived in France. You should mention:
- the journey through France
- how you met the people fleeing the war zone
- your first contact with wounded soldiers
- first impressions of the trenches.

Think about the *tone* of your letter. You need to decide how much to tell your family of the dangers and of the terrible sights you have already seen. How do you want them to feel? How much of the truth should you tell them? Do you want to worry them?

End your letter with the words:

Don't worry, I'll soon be back.

● When you have finished a *first draft*, let a partner read it and help you to improve it. Write your *final* version.

● Then write a reply to Will, imagining that you are his mother, sister or father. In this letter, you will need to respond to some of the things Will has told you, but also tell him your news, about the family and village.

What do you think Will's family knows about the war? Perhaps not much. Maybe Will's letter has shocked and surprised them.

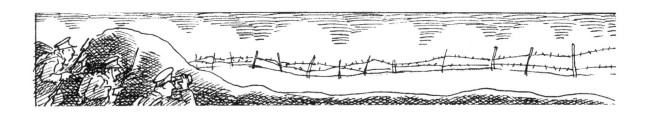

Is sport like war?

Listen to the way people talk about and write about sport and you'd think so!

'They were prepared to go out there tonight and die for their team.'
(Ron Atkinson, TV commentator, on the England v Italy World Cup
qualifying match, October 1997)

The lads at the start of *War Game* go off to war thinking it is going to be an
'adventure', another version of the football game they play.

The following words are about fighting and warfare, but they are sometimes used
to describe sporting 'battles'.
● Work with a partner. For each word, write a sentence that uses it to describe sport.
Then swap pages and write a sentence that uses the same word to describe war.

attack	war	At daybreak we began to attack the enemy lines.
	sport	In the second half we attacked their goal continually.
victory	war	
	sport	
defeat	war	
	sport	
defend	war	
	sport	
battle	war	
	sport	
shoot	war	
	sport	
tactics	war	
	sport	
campaign	war	
	sport	
contest	war	
	sport	

● Give as many reasons as you can for why the book is called *War Game*.

Writing dialogue

● Re-read the following section from the beginning of the book.

> "We'll come back and beat you after the war," laughed one of the opposing team as they began their walk back to the village five miles away.
>   "Most of them are joining the army," said Freddie, the goalkeeper. "We should, really."
>   "I'd like to," said Billy, eyes shining with excitement.

● Notice that Michael Foreman writes the conversation (or dialogue) so that it is clear who is speaking. Look carefully to see how he shows when someone starts speaking and when they finish speaking. The actual words that are spoken have been circled.

● Can you complete these *rules* for writing dialogue?

> Use *speech marks* **before**
>
> Put a *punctuation mark* **after**
>
> Use *speech marks* **after**
>
> Start a *new line* for

This next bit of the dialogue has had all the speech punctuation removed.

> No, you're too young. If you went, I'd have to go to look after you, laughed his big brother Lacey. It *would* be an adventure though, said Will. And they say it'll be over by Christmas. Be a pity to miss it.

● Using the *rules* for writing dialogue, write this bit of the conversation and see how accurately you can put all the speech punctuation back in. Remember to start a new line for a different speaker. Use a separate sheet of paper.

● Check your version with a partner, and then look at the original section in the book.

Writing dialogue (cont.)

Now it's your turn to write some dialogue.
As the lads walk back to the village after the match they chat about the war and how they feel about joining up.

● In your small group, improvise the conversation. You could clear a space, get up and walk slowly along, as if you are the lads strolling towards the village.

Remember: the lads are excited by the idea of going off to fight. Some of them might talk about it as if it were just another game of football. One or two of them may be more worried about it than others.

● When you have worked on your conversation and made it as good as you can, write out the dialogue. You don't need to remember it word for word. There were probably four or five different people talking.

Remember to follow your *rules* for writing dialogue. If you're not sure, look back to page 20.

You might like to begin your conversation like this:

"And they say it will be over by Christmas. Be a pity to miss it," said Will.

In memoriam

The phrase 'in memoriam' is Latin and means 'in memory'. It is often used to *commemorate* someone after they have died. Can you see the connection between:

In (memoriam)   (Memory)   Com(memo)rate

● Read these short poems which were written by soldiers who fought in the First World War. Each commemorates the death of so many young men.

In Memoriam (Easter, 1915)

Why do the flowers remind the poet of men? — (The flowers left thick) at nightfall in the wood

This Eastertide call into mind the men,

Now (far from home,) who, with their (sweethearts,) should — girlfriends?

away fighting in France — Have gathered them and (will do never again.)

Why? Died in the war

The Cherry Trees

The cherry trees bend over and are shedding,

On the old road where all that passed are dead,

Their petals, strewing the grass as for a wedding

This early May morn when there is none to wed.

Both poems written by Edward Thomas (1878–1917)
Killed at Arras, 9th April 1917

Here Dead Lie We

Here dead lie we because we did not choose

To live and shame the land from which we sprung.

Life, to be sure, is nothing much to lose;

But young men think it is, and we were young.

A E Housman (1859–1936)

● Now, with a partner, re-read the poems and *annotate* each one as you go. You could:

- jot down questions about bits you don't understand
- explain words or phrases
- pick out sections you like or think are interesting
- show what the poem makes you think of or see in your mind
- think about the 'mood' or 'tone' of the poem.

The first one has been started for you, so you can see what to do.

● Imagine that the people in Will's village decide to commemorate the deaths of the lads from the village football team. It's your job to write a short 'In Memoriam' poem to go on the memorial. Another word for this kind of writing is *epitaph*.

Think about what you want your poem to say. Do you wish it to suggest that the lads were heroes? Or were they 'sacrificed'? Will the tone of the poem be sad, proud, bitter or angry? What do you want people to feel as they read the lines?

● Read again the three poems on page 22. See if you can say what you want to say in *four short lines*, too. Don't copy the poems, but try to do the same sort of thing in your lines.

Do some planning first.
● In the box opposite, make a list of words, phrases, images (pictures in words) and ideas for your lines.

● Now try to arrange them into some kind of order. Think about the mood or tone of what you are saying.

● Ask a partner to read what you have drafted and to give you advice. What works well? What isn't clear or could be improved? Revise and edit your lines, and work on a final draft. Use a separate sheet of paper.

● Give your poem a title before writing a best copy, perhaps using an outline of a war memorial.

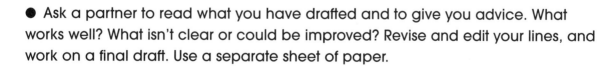

Winter warfare

As the war dragged on into the winter of 1914–1915, life in the trenches was made much worse by the bitter cold.

Edgell Rickword wrote the poem 'Winter Warfare' to show how winter affected the troops. He describes winter as if it were a person, using both German ('Hauptmann Kälte') and English ('Colonel Cold'). This clever idea helps him to link the difficulties caused by winter with the dangers of war.

● With a partner, read 'Winter Warfare' aloud, taking a verse each. Then swap around so that you read each other's verses.

Winter Warfare

the shoulder 'tabs' on a soldier's uniform

thick white frost

the line of trenches

a sharp point worn on the back of a boot by a horse rider, used to 'spur' on the horse

Colonel Cold strode up the Line
(tabs) of rime and spurs of ice);
stiffened all that met his glare:
    horses, men, and lice.

Visited a forward post,
  left them burning, ear to foot;
fingers stuck to biting steel,
    toes to frozen boot.

Stalked on into No Man's Land,
  turned the wire to fleecy wool,
iron stakes to sugar sticks
    snapping at a pull.

barbed wire

a favourite sweet – sugary sticks to suck

Those who watched with hoary eyes
  saw two figures gleaming there;
Hauptmann Kälte, Colonel Cold,
  gaunt in the grey air.

German for 'Colonel Cold'

'hoar' frost turns everything to white; here, soldiers' eyebrows are turned white with cold

Stiffly, tinkling spurs they moved,
  glassy-eyed, with glinting heel
stabbing those who lingered there
    torn by screaming steel.

wounded soldiers in No Man's Land

shells and bullets

Winter warfare (cont.)

● Look carefully at the explanations of some of the vocabulary. Talk about these images.

‘strode up the Line’   ‘spurs of ice’
‘two figures gleaming there’   ‘Stiffly, tinkling spurs they moved’

Can you see how each image could be a description of both a person and the winter?

● What does the freezing cold do to the men and to the battlefield? Use the grid to list the changes that happen. The first two have been done for you.

What winter does	
phrase	*meaning*
‘stiffened all that met his glare’	The men are stiff with cold. Also they have to stand to attention (stiffen) when the Colonel passes.
‘Visited a forward post, left them burning, ear to foot; fingers stuck to biting steel, toes to frozen boot.’	When your ears freeze they feel like they are burning.
‘Stalked on into No Man’s Land’	
‘turned the wire to fleecy wool’	
‘stabbing those who lingered there torn by screaming steel’	

● With a partner, look at the illustrations on the last pages of the book, starting at the page that begins ‘Two more days passed peacefully’.

● Choose *one* illustration that you think goes well with the poem ‘Winter Warfare’. Which images from the poem can you see in the illustration you’ve chosen? Explain why you chose this picture, then read out just those lines or phrases from the poem which you think fit it.

Will's nightmare of war

Will's final thoughts are: 'Thank God. We'll all have a game when this nightmare's over.'

● Think back over the whole story. What things have added up to make Will's experience of war a 'nightmare', something he wishes he could wake up from and find had never happened?
Make a list (it's been started for you):

Will's nightmare of war

Seeing families fleeing, with a few possessions
Seeing exhausted, wounded soldiers

● Compare your list with a partner. Then in a small group, talk about the ending of *War Game*. Use these points to get you started:

● What do you *think* and *feel* about how the story ends?
● How well do you think Michael Foreman finishes the story?
● 'He closed his eyes.' These are the last words in the whole book. Why do you think Michael Foreman chooses to end the book in this way?

Remember to listen carefully to the ideas of others in your group, and to explain your ideas carefully.

War Game talk log

● After about five to ten minutes of talking, fill in the *talk log* to record the ideas and to capture your own thoughts about the book.

Five interesting ideas that we discussed are:

1

2

3

4

5

Some of the ideas I put forward are:

Talking in a group did/did not help me to think more about the book because

If someone said, 'So, what's War Game really about?' I would answer (don't be tempted to retell the story; say what the story *means* to you):

War Game is a moving story. At a general level, it tells of the human cost of war; it tells and, more importantly depicts, the experiences of one group of country lads (based on Foreman's own uncles) and their experiences of the horrors of the trenches.

War Game is a collage of a book. Foreman mixes memorabilia and photographs of artefacts from the period of the First World War (1914–18) with his own original watercolours. He also places information text (captions, factual descriptions) alongside a stark narrative that often takes second place to the depictions in his artwork. The book can and should be read on these different levels in order to make coherence of the whole text. Foreman's artwork is mesmerizing and detailed. It captures the horror and brutality of trench warfare and the spirit of the period.

MANAGING THE READING OF *WAR GAME*

The 'Ways in' activities are designed to prompt children to investigate the setting of the story, and to build up some key historical details. They encourage children to explore the kind of story *War Game* might be and to begin to see how artwork and written text interact to create joint meaning. The 'Ways in' activities should be carried out before the book is read.

Children then read the book in eight sections, each of which is supported by a 'Making sense' activity. This structure enables children to look very closely at the way the narrative is constructed and to use their

developing knowledge of the story to make confident predictions and to anticipate events. The eight sections are:
• up to the words 'And so they talked as they wandered along the dusty lane into the village'
• up to the end of the first chapter, 'The Kick-off
• up to the words 'They had a lot of explaining to do when they got home that evening' in the second chapter 'The Adventure'
• up to the words 'It seemed like a pretty good war so far, even though it had begun to rain and the long dry summer was over' in the third chapter, 'To the Front'
• up to the words 'Doesn't it look pretty? Just like fireworks' in the third chapter
• up to the words '…and a shooting match would develop accompanied by cheers and boos' in the final chapter, 'No Man's Land'
• up to the words 'Good night, Fritz. We'll have another game'
• up to the end of the book.

'Developing ideas' prompt children to re-read and reflect on specific sections and key themes, and to explore the narrative technique of the book.

CLASSROOM MANAGEMENT AND SUPPORT

War Game can be shared by the class, but the children should have access to the pictures as well as the text as the two elements work so closely together as a whole. Intersperse reading the book as a class with discussion of the section that has just been read.

Many of the activities are suitable for group, pair or individual work. The following are particularly suitable for children collaborating either as pairs or in small groups of four to six:
'Getting a sense of the story' (page 7)
'A lot of explaining to do' (page 10)
'The ending' (page 16)
'Writing dialogue' (pages 20–21)
'In memoriam' (pages 22–23)
'Will's nightmare of war' (page 26) and '*War Game* talk log' (Page 27).

DIFFERENTIATION

This book provides a range of activities for you to match and adapt to the needs and abilities of your class. Most of them are designed to be accessible to children in Years 5 and 6 (P6/P7) and differentiation will come from their differing levels of response.

The more challenging activities are 'In memoriam' (pages 22–23) and 'Winter warfare' (pages 24–25). Less able children may need teacher support to work on these. Most of the activities provide the basis of response work which can be extended as you wish. The teachers' notes give ideas for extension tasks which have been devised to challenge more able readers and writers.

TIME-SCALE

An uninterrupted reading of *War Game* would take only about one hour, but it is not a book to be rushed through. Time would be well spent examining the detail, mood and focus of the illustrations and reading the captions. The aim of *Read & Respond* is to slow down the reading of the book in order to improve the quality of children's response. If you make *War Game* the focus of your English work, plan to work with the book over a two to three week period. This would give children enough time to reflect and delve deeper into the text and to practise reader-response skills, without diluting the enjoyment of the book by overloading them.

MATCHING THE BOOK TO YOUR CLASS

War Game is a simple story but a complex book. It can of course be read aloud, but access to the pictures is vital for it to come alive to children. It is well worth investing in at least one copy of the hardback edition (or the new paperback edition published by Pavilion), as it is in colour and in a different format – changes which transform the reading experience.

It is part memoir, part fiction, part non-fiction – a fascinating amalgam of styles and genres. For this reason it can be read on many different levels and has very wide appeal. The vocabulary used makes it challenging in parts, but the high-interest level of the themes and the story will motivate children to find out meanings. The captions and the information elements too provide a mine of additional information, and of course Foreman's stunning artwork carries readers along.

TEACHING POTENTIAL OF *WAR GAME*

War Game offers the following learning opportunities:

Writing
- extended diary, letter and journal writing
- dialogue and speech punctuation
- imaginative, descriptive writing.

Literary understanding and response
- empathetic writing – seeing things from the point of view of the central character
- close reading and response to story
- persuasive texts (recruiting posters).

Responding to language
- vocabulary work, working out unfamiliar words from their context
- persuasive language
- archaisms and other features of texts written in an 'older' style.

Cross-curricular links
- history study (investigating the 1914–18 war)
- art (children developing their ability to analyse and respond to Foreman's evocative illustrations).

GLOSSARY

It would be helpful, though not essential, if children know the following key terms. Always teach them in the context of an activity. Encourage children to use these terms in their own discussion or written work: author, illustrator, image and imagery, dialogue and freeze frame.

PRIOR TEACHING

Some activities may be more successful if you teach using a model for children to follow first. The following activities would benefit from this approach:
'Will's diary (1) The football game' (page 8)
'In memoriam' (pages 22–23)
'Winter warfare' (pages 24–25).

RESOURCES

As mentioned above, it would be well worth purchasing a copy of the hardback edition of *War Game* (Pavilion Books Ltd) or the new paperback edition (also published by Pavilion). For wider reading, the following books will also be useful for more able readers, or for reading selected passages aloud.

Other books by Michael Foreman:
War Boy: A Country Childhood (Puffin)
After the War Was Over (Puffin)
Grandfather's Pencil and the Room of Stories (Red Fox)

Other First World War books:
First World War by Terry Deary from the *Horrible Histories* series (Hippo Books)
Prose Anthology of the First World War by Robert Hull (Wayland)
Poetry of the First World War by Edward Hudson (Wayland)
Farm Boy by Michael Morpurgo and Michael Foreman (Pavilion)
Summer of the Zeppelin by Elsie McCutcheon (Collins)

COVER COMPARISON (PAGE 4)

Aims: to examine the covers; to develop the skills of comparison; to speculate about the hints that the covers and title provide as to the content of the story.

Teaching points: the cover of the paperback version (Cover A) presents a greater sense of the war and the darker side to the story; the hardback cover (Cover B) offers a lighter, more optimistic view, showing the two 'sides' playing football. Help children to draw out these differences and to think about what each might make the reader think the book is about and what kind of story to expect.

WHAT DO YOU KNOW ABOUT THE FIRST WORLD WAR? (PAGE 5)

Aim: to enable children to 'preview' their existing knowledge about the First World War.

Teaching points: Teach the children how to construct a 'mind map' first, by using an 'easier' subject, perhaps based on a recently covered topic. They will need to see how to distinguish between main branches and side branches, and to follow through connections between bits of knowledge. The example on the photocopiable page begins to do this for the First World War. You may well want to add information of your own to spark off more ideas from the children. Children's knowledge of the Great War may be fragmentary; some will know more than others.

Extension: ask the children to look at the dedication at the start of the book: *In memory of my uncles, who died in the Great War...* Suggest that they look up the word 'dedication' in a dictionary. Ask them to think about why the author has dedicated his book to these people.

THE GREATER GAME (PAGE 6)

Aims: discussion of the 'recruiting' of soldiers; to introduce persuasive language.

Teaching points: if possible, make an enlarged photocopy of the picture of the poster on page 6 so that it can be used as part of a shared reading session with the whole class. This will provide plenty of opportunity for discussion. The children should think about the period of history depicted. What are the clues that this is many years ago? Focus on the double meaning of 'field' as preparation for the way that Michael Foreman links football and fighting throughout the story. Discuss 'honour' by finding dictionary definitions and thinking about connected words: 'honourable', 'dishonour', 'respect' and 'esteem', for example. Do the same for the other key words.

Extension: children can design their own recruiting poster, either individually or in pairs, by drafting ideas out first and choosing an image that will persuade young men to enlist.

They should write appropriate text, using all four words that they have just looked up, that is, 'honour', 'enlist', 'patriotic' and 'recruit' (explain that these can be changed in order for them to be fitted into a sentence, for example 'enlist' to 'enlisting'), as well as other useful words and phrases such as 'forward to victory', 'for King and country, 'join up now' and 'don't delay'. Arrange a display of the posters, followed by discussion of persuasive effects. Look at the enlarged photocopy of the recruiting poster again to consider features of language and persuasion.

GETTING A SENSE OF THE STORY (PAGE 7)

Aim: further speculation about the content and shape of the book by looking at the chapter headings.

Teaching points: children should work with a partner to discuss the headings and present their ideas to the rest of their group or to the whole class. The twin themes of sport, excitement and adventure, and the hints of something darker and more menacing, should be the focus of the discussion. For the question asking the children about where the story is set, preferably read the opening three pages of the book aloud, and ask them to respond to the establishment of a place and a time. What are the clues? (Rural, village life, early 20th century transport, at the eve of a war, and so on.) The writing of the characters' thoughts for the final part of the page should be done individually, children re-reading the opening and then transferring either the actual words or adding their own ideas to show the sense of anticipation and excitement the story creates.

WILL'S DIARY (1) THE FOOTBALL GAME (PAGE 8)

Aims: to deepen understanding of the effect of the war on the central character; to introduce a specific form of writing.

Teaching points: this is the first of a series of similar tasks which guide readers through the key moments in the story. Supplement the two short examples of diaries given on the photocopiable page with some more of your own. These extracts are from *The War the Infantry Knew 1914–1919* by Captain JC Dunn (Jane's Publishing Co. Ltd) and *Anne Frank: The Diary of a Young Girl* edited by Otto H Frank and Mirjam Pressler (Viking).

Deal with the 'Rules for diary writing' as a whole-class activity, and follow it with some modelling of how to go about writing the first diary entry for Will, using the opening line provided. (Remind the children that diary entries should have a date and ask them to check that they have included important details such as Will's feelings about the war.)

Note: for all the diary activities (see pages 8, 11 and 14), children can use a photocopy of page 9.

A LOT OF EXPLAINING TO DO (PAGE 10)

Aims: to deepen understanding of character; to introduce 'scripting dialogue' in drama.

Teaching points: ideally, use a large space to run the improvisation work, with the whole class divided into small groups of three or four. Explain that each group should be in role as Will and his family. You could tell the children to construct a freeze-frame (a still picture) of a key moment in the conversation – perhaps when Will reveals that he has joined up. Each group in turn then either 'runs' that section of their improvisation, or alternatively, you can 'track' the thoughts of each character by tapping him or her on the shoulder and asking, 'Who are you and what are you thinking now?'

The written scripting needs to follow the 'shape' of the dialogue rather than capture it exactly. Make sure the children understand the conventions of setting up a script by modelling this for them first.

Extension: ask the children to write the scene as a conversation with narrative, giving them the following opening:

That evening Will returned home later than usual. As he opened the back door, he called out, 'I'm home, mother!' His mother looked up.

WILL'S DIARY (2) TO THE FRONT (PAGE 11)

Aims: to focus children's attention on the details of the time at the training camp and the journey to France and the Front; to gather, sort and classify factual information, and differentiate this from the character's thoughts and feelings.

Teaching points: it is better if this is carried out as a group activity so that children can each have a copy of the book. Before children turn to the diary, which should be an individual writing task, they can work together, searching the relevant sections of the story for information to include in it.

THEN THINGS BEGAN TO CHANGE (PAGES 12–13)

Aim: close reading and response, including deduction and inference.

Teaching points: this is a focused activity that requires children to re-read the key section describing the effect of the war on ordinary people, and to trace Will's changing perspective. To promote the deductive reading required to answer the questions, model the correct lines of thinking through class or group discussion first. The emphasis should be on 'what the passage tells us' and 'what the passage doesn't tell us, but is hinted at or implied'.

The vocabulary activity is an opportunity to show children how to 'work out' the meaning of a word in its context.

Extension: in pairs, children can find another short passage from the story so far (for example, the section dealing with the training camp: 'Being country boys... the days were long and exhausting') and write their own questions which require deductive and inferential reading for other pairs to attempt.

WILL'S DIARY (3) THE FRONT LINE (PAGE 14)

Aims: to think carefully and empathetically about Will's experience of life in the trenches, and to draw together a range of information and link it to his changing feelings about the war; to organize ideas via the use of a set of writing 'prompts'.

Teaching points: children will need time to re-read the section, and to make notes on what Will is to include in his diary entry. The 'prompts' are just that – a series of reminders and suggestions to guide the writer and to present an overview of the writing task.

WILL'S POSTCARD – CHRISTMAS (PAGE 15)

Aims: to link the original text of a letter with the section of the story; to develop the skills of summary and concise use of language.

Teaching points: ask pairs of children to read the letter aloud to each other, before discussing 'style' either with the whole class or with a group. Focus on 'archaisms' (for example, 'a very nice set of fellows', 'Nanny') and the tone of the letter (it is very upbeat; there is no mention of the terrible conditions). To write the postcard, suggest that the children practise one first, so that they can get used to the idea of conveying a lot of information in a limited number of words.

THE ENDING (PAGE 16)

Aim: close reading and response to the way that the author chooses to finish the book.

Teaching points: children will need to have an individual copy of the book in order to carry out the necessary re-reading. There are ample opportunities for pair and small group discussion following this activity – children can compare ideas and discuss their interpretations. Refer children back to the earlier activities 'Cover comparison' (page 4) and 'Getting a sense of the story' (page 7) in which they were predicting the kind of story and how it might develop.

NO MAN'S LAND (PAGE 17)

Aim: close observation of one of Michael Foreman's illustrations.

Teaching points: this is an individual task, with opportunities for comparison and discussion later. It is important to ensure that the children select from a range of illustrations, rather than restricting their choice to one or two – they can then 'test out' the accuracy of their descriptions on each other later. Less confident writers will benefit from being taken carefully through the process with you, or another adult, as a guide at each stage.

THOSE LEFT BEHIND (PAGE 18)

Aim: to use letter form, incorporating planning, drafting and revision.

Teaching points: in this activity the children plan and write a first draft, then work with a 'response partner'. This stage will need careful explanation and modelling if they are not used to commenting on each other's drafts. It is important that they comment on the content, organization and tone of the letter, using the prompt questions on the activity sheet. Children should go through the same process with the reply to Will's letter, swapping with a partner and helping with improvements.

IS SPORT LIKE WAR? (PAGE 19)

Aims: to highlight the way that language can be used literally (as in the case of war) and metaphorically (the use of the vocabulary of war in a sporting context); to focus attention on the implications of the title of the story.

Teaching points: this sheet is for pair work; encourage the children to talk through their ideas before committing themselves to paper. Use the first example which is provided in the text as a class or group teaching point.

WRITING DIALOGUE (PAGES 20–21)

Aims: to focus on accurate use of speech punctuation and layout for a conversation in a sentence-level activity.

Teaching points: children are asked to derive the rules for writing speech punctuation from the example provided. Once a set of workable rules have been agreed, these could be displayed as a wall poster in the classroom. Although the activity has a self-checking procedure built into it, you may want to draw the group or class back together to review the activity and to reinforce the teaching points.

The second part of the activity will be best carried out if the whole class is working on it at the same time, so that you can organize the drama/improvisation element.

IN MEMORIAM (PAGES 22–23)

Aims: close reading and response to poetry; to deepen understanding of the way that the story conveys the sense of loss and sacrifice of a whole generation of young men.

Teaching points: this is a challenging activity that is designed to stretch the more able children, those already working at and above Level 4. It has been set up so that individual children will be adequately supported if they are working at it alone, but it will be best handled by you working with children on the first of the short poems, before expecting them to carry on without direct support. Children should be encouraged to read the poems over to themselves (and aloud to each other) several times, to get a sense of the 'tune' of the poem before embarking on the annotation.

Completed epitaphs can be displayed around the classroom, along with illustrations or suitably selected photographs.

WINTER WARFARE (PAGES 24–25)

Aim: to introduce a First World War poem, one which has powerful resonances to the content of *War Game*.

Teaching points: as with the previous activity, this has been designed to extend children working at the higher levels, but can also be taught as a whole-class shared-reading focus, possibly after a more able group have attempted it. In this way their ideas and responses can be incorporated into the whole-class work.

The activity slows the reading of the poem down and then offers children a structure for thinking about how the writer personifies the cold as an army colonel, striding up and down the line, freezing the men and transforming the landscape. There are a series of illustrations in the latter part of the book that the poem has direct parallels with.

WILL'S NIGHTMARE OF WAR AND *WAR GAME* TALK LOG (PAGES 26–27)

Aim: to think back over the whole story and to come to conclusions about the ending of the book and what it conveys about the First World War.

Teaching points: children will need to have a copy of the book in order to look back and complete the listing activity. Working with a partner, they should compare lists, then discuss the ending. It will help to support their talk if you establish expectations for what should be going on in the discussion and list these for everyone to see. The 'talk log' will encourage reflection both on the content of the discussion and its value.

Extension: draw the whole class together once pairs and groups have finished discussing and have completed the talk log. Compare a) reflections on the discussion (Was it of value? What ideas emerged?) and b) children's responses to the *big* question at the end – 'So, what's *War Game* really about?'